SEVEN MEN AT DAYBREAK

"A blessed companion is a book"—JERROLD